THE BOOK OF THINGS THAT MAKE me HAPPY

igloobooks

igloobooks

Published in 2021
First published in the UK by Igloo Books Ltd
An imprint of Igloo Books Ltd
Cottage Farm, NN6 0BJ, UK
Owned by Bonnier Books
Sveavägen 56, Stockholm, Sweden
www.igloobooks.com

0821 001
2 4 6 8 10 9 7 5 3 1
ISBN 978-1-80022-458-2

Designed by Simon Parker
Edited by Hannah Cather

Printed and manufactured in China

This journal belongs to:

....

WHAT MAKES ME HAPPY?

Whether it's spending time with loved ones or watching a beautiful sunrise, you probably have an idea of what makes you happy. But now it's time to tap into your thoughts and feelings, and discover what really matters to you at your core.

A life filled with happiness and joy is achievable, but only you can make this happen. With the help of this journal, you'll be able to identify your life goals, passions and values, and start to create the life that you deserve.

HOW TO USE THIS JOURNAL:

Inside, you'll find a series of questions and creative exercises to help you reflect on what makes you happy. Using this journal is the perfect way to celebrate all the amazing things in your life and to find out more about yourself.

You may wish to work through the journal from beginning to end, or you might prefer to flip to a random page and start there — it's completely up to you. Start with a positive attitude and don't be afraid to have fun along the way!

TODAY IS THE PERFECT DAY TO BE HAPPY

What does happiness mean to you?

Decorate this page with thoughts and doodles.

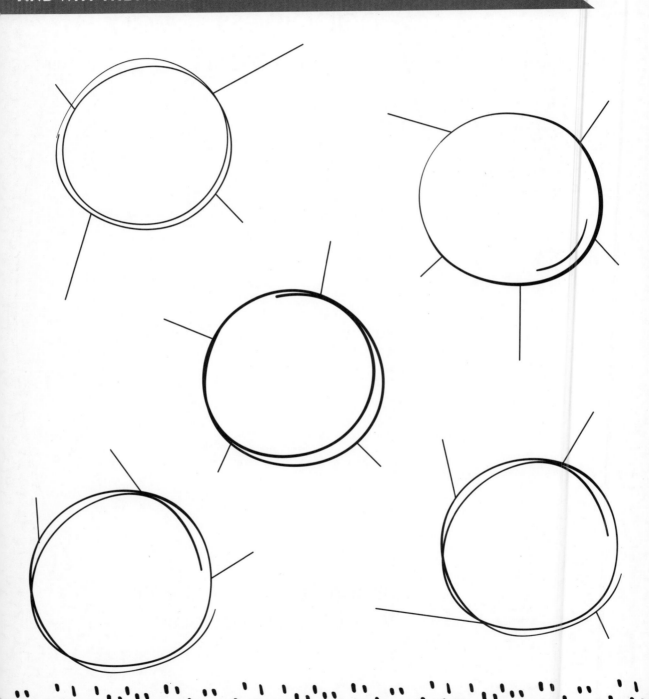

1 ....

2 ....

NOTE DOWN
TEN OF YOUR
BEST QUALITIES.
PERHAPS YOU'RE A
GREAT LISTENER
OR AWESOME
AT MAKING
PEOPLE LAUGH.

3 ....

4 ....

5 ....

6 ....

7 ....

8 ....

9 ....

10 ....

Think back to a time when you made a loved one feel happy...

What did you do?

How did you feel?

When and where?

Was anyone else involved?

Think back to one of your proudest moments...

What did you do?

What was going through your mind?

Was anyone else there?

Have you done anything like it since?

MY RECIPE FOR HAPPINESS

You can add anything you like into the mix!
How about warm weather, good company and laughter?

A SPRINKLE OF...

A HANDFUL OF...

A SPOONFUL OF...

A PINCH OF...

A CUP OF...

A DOZEN...

PLAN YOUR PERFECT DINNER PARTY

The details:

Who's invited?

....

When and where?

....

What's on the menu?

Appetizer: ....

Main Course: ....

Dessert: ....

How will you decorate the table?

....

Who will you sit next to?

....

Topics of conversation?

....

Will it be casual or formal?

....

How long will it go on for?

....

MY MOST PRIZED POSSESSION

Draw a picture of your most prized possession below:

Why is it so important to you?

....

Did someone give it to you? If so, who?

....

What's the story behind it?

....

Where do you keep it?

....

MY DREAM PURCHASE

What is it?

....

Where would you buy it?

....

How would owning it make you feel?

....

What would it add to your life?

....

LIVE YOUR LIFE BY A COMPASS,
NOT A CLOCK.

IMAGINE THAT YOU ARE ON A JOURNEY TO A NEW DESTINATION...

WHERE ARE YOU GOING?

WHAT CAN YOU SEE?

WHAT IS THE FIRST THING YOU'LL DO?

WHO IS WITH YOU?

My Feel-Good Movie

Think of a movie that makes you really happy.

What is it about?

What makes it so great?

Which characters do you love the most?

How do you feel when you watch it?

My Happy Song
Think of your go-to song for good vibes.

Song title: Artist:

Which lyrics do you love the most?

When did you first hear it?

Who, or what, does it remind you of?

Doodle Your Happy Place

Are there any
people there?

Why does it
make you
happy?

What will you
do there?

What can you
see and hear?

A yoga mat

Candles

Essential oils

Ice cream

A full bookshelf

Fresh flowers

A poster of your idol

Design your perfect space to relax in.
Feel free to use the items above!

My Memory Box

Imagine a box where you can keep your happiest memories.

Which memories would you put inside?

Why are these memories so special to you?

Are any of these memories from your childhood?

If you could relive one of them, which would it be and why?

How do you feel when you think about them now?

USE THE SQUARES TO CREATE A HAPPINESS REEL OF YOUR YEAR SO FAR. WHAT HAVE BEEN THE BIGGEST HIGHLIGHTS?

NOW USE THE SQUARES TO PLAN YOUR HAPPINESS REEL FOR NEXT YEAR. WHAT WOULD YOU LIKE IT TO CONTAIN?

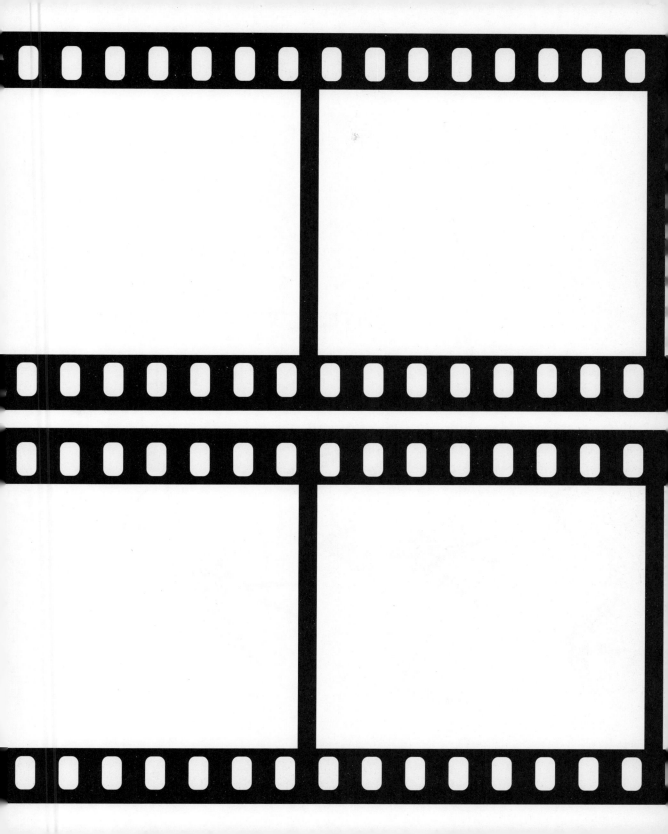

THE GREATEST LUXURY
IS BEING FREE

Use your five senses to discover all the things you love in the world around you.

I love to see:

....

....

I love the smell of:

....

....

I love to hear:

....

....

I love to touch:

....

....

I love to taste:

....

....

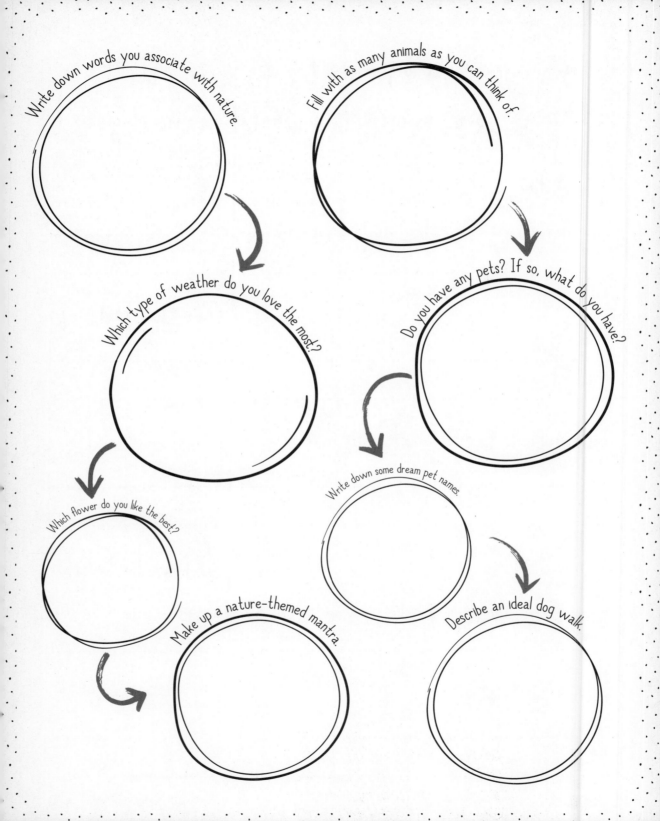

Write down words you associate with nature.

Fill with as many animals as you can think of.

Which type of weather do you love the most?

Do you have any pets? If so, what do you have?

Which flower do you like the best?

Write down some dream pet names.

Make up a nature-themed mantra.

Describe an ideal dog walk.

This is a happiness fountain.
Write down all the happy words you can think of in the water!

Amazing Trips

Where did you go?
....

....
What made you decide to
go there?
....

Why was it so great?
....
Would you ever go back again? Why/why not?

....

Where did you go?
....

....
What made you decide to
go there?
....
Why was it so great?
....
Would you ever go back again? Why/why not?
....

DREAM DESTINATIONS

Where?
....
....
Who would you go with?
....
....
What time of year would you go?
....
List things you would love to do there:
....
....

Where?
....
Who would you go with?
....
....
What time of year would you go?
....
List things you would love to do there:
....
....

Happiness
Blooms
from
Within

THE COLD OF A CRISP WINTER EVENING.

THIS IS A HAPPINESS PLANT. ON EACH LEAF, WRITE DOWN ANYTHING IN NATURE THAT MAKES YOU HAPPY.

DREAM JOB

Write down your dream job:

....

Would you work for a company or for yourself?

....

Would you work from home or from an office?

....

What would the job entail?

....

....

....

Why would this be your perfect job?

....

....

....

DESIGN YOUR PERFECT WORKSPACE.
WOULD ANY OF THE BELOW APPEAR IN IT?

A coffee machine

Glass walls

A vending machine

A view of the city

The best laptop on the market

Beautiful stationary

A pool table

My closest friends

The name of my friend:...

What do you like most about them? ....
Write down one of your inside jokes: ....
What is one of your best memories together? ....
What makes your friendship so great? ....

The name of my friend:...

What do you like most about them? ....
Write down one of your inside jokes: ....
What is one of your best memories together? ....
What makes your friendship so great? ....

The name of my friend:...

What do you like most about them? ....
Write down one of your inside jokes: ....
What is one of your best memories together? ....
What makes your friendship so great? ....

MY HERO

My hero's name:

....

What amazing things have they done?

....
....

What are some of their best qualities?

....
....

Why do you admire them so much?

....
....

What is the most heroic thing they've
ever done?

....
....

DO EVERYTHING
IN LIFE WITH
PASSION
& DETERMINATION

What are some of your proudest achievements? Write them in order, with 1 being the achievement that made you happiest.

Happiest

1

2

3

4

5

1

2

3

4

5

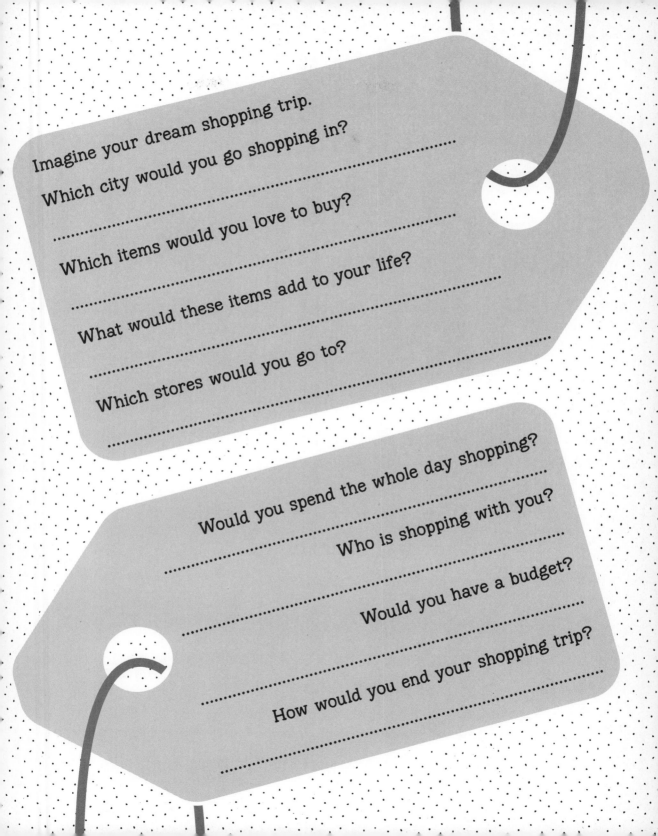

Imagine your dream shopping trip.

Which city would you go shopping in?

....

Which items would you love to buy?

....

What would these items add to your life?

....

Which stores would you go to?

....

Would you spend the whole day shopping?

....

Who is shopping with you?

....

Would you have a budget?

....

How would you end your shopping trip?

....

Health & Happiness

The form of exercise I enjoy the most is:

....

Why do you enjoy it so much?

....

....

Where do you like to do it?

....

....

What are its health benefits?

....

....

Which emotions do you normally
experience during it?

....

....

My perfect workout

What time will the workout start?

....

....

Where will it take place?

....

....

What will the workout consist of?

....

....

....

....

How long will it last?

....

....

You are
the most
valuable
investment
you will ever
make

My self-care evening

Plan in some me-time!

What kinds of things would you do to relax?

....

....

Which snacks and treats would you eat?

....

When will you have your next self-care evening?

....

For the evening to be a success, what must it include?

....

....

....

WHAT TIME OF DAY MAKES YOU HAPPY?

Circle which time you like the most.

Have you always preferred this time of day?

....

What do you enjoy doing during this time?

....

Are you most productive during this time?

....

WHAT TIME OF YEAR MAKES YOU HAPPY?

Circle which one you like the most.

Why does this season make you happy?

....

Are there any special events occurring in this season?

....

What do you like to wear?

....

What three things do you love to see?

....

1

2

3

4

List five random
acts of kindness
you could do
for people in
your life.

5

What five things could someone do for you to make you happy?

1

2

3

4

5

GO WHERE YOU FEEL THE MOST ALIVE

What was the last special event you attended that made you feel happy?

EVENT:

. . . .

WHEN AND WHERE?

. . . .

WHO DID YOU GO WITH?

. . . .

TOP HIGHLIGHT?

. . . .

HOW DID YOU FEEL AT THE END OF IT?

. . . .

What does your
invention do?

What does it
look like?

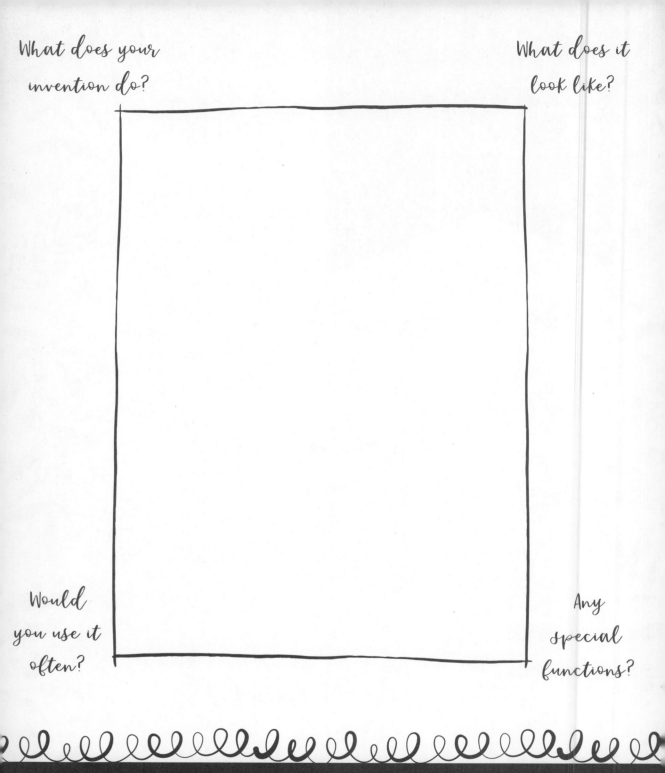

Would
you use it
often?

Any
special
functions?

DESIGN AND DOODLE AN INVENTION THAT WOULD MAKE YOU HAPPY. BE AS CREATIVE AS YOU LIKE!

I am always
attracting
abundance

I deserve to
be loved just
as I am

I am
choosing to
be happy

Think of four important people in your life. What makes them happy?

Person 1:

....

Person 2:

....

Person 3:

....

Person 4:

....

Write down compliments for them below, and check them off as you say them!

Compliments

....

....

....

Compliments

....

....

....

Compliments

....

....

....

Compliments

....

....

....

Wherever you are
right now, let it
teach you something.

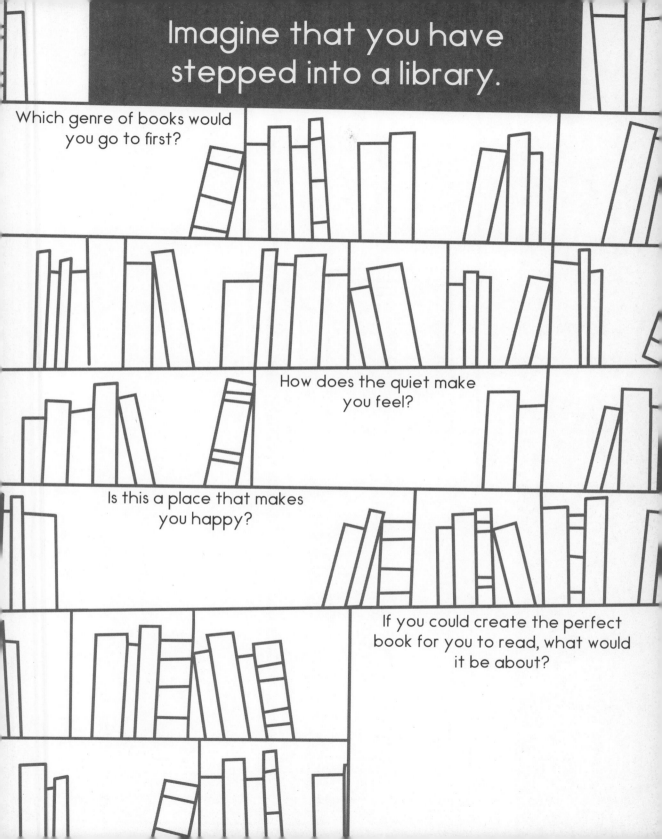

Cover this fridge in happy magnets.

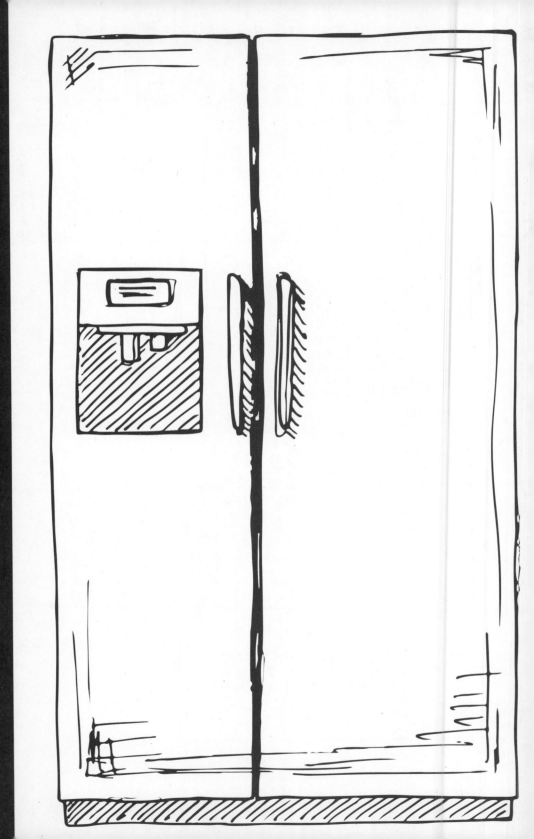

CHILDHOOD
MEMORIES

LIST FIVE THINGS THAT MADE YOU HAPPY AS A CHILD:

....

....

....

WHY DID THESE THINGS MAKE YOU SO HAPPY?

....

....

....

HOW DO THEY COMPARE TO WHAT MAKES YOU HAPPY NOW?

....

....

WHAT IS YOUR MOST TREASURED CHILDHOOD MEMORY?

....

....

DAILY ROUTINE

USE THE PLANNER TO MAP OUT YOUR IDEAL DAILY ROUTINE.
IT DOESN'T HAVE TO ALIGN WITH YOUR LIFE RIGHT NOW.

EARLY MORNING	MID MORNING	AFTERNOON	EVENING	NIGHT

WORKOUT

NOTES
- -
- -
- -

GOALS

My plan for creating a fulfilled life

Note down three rules for making the most of life:

....

....

....

What's the one thing you need for a fulfilling life?

....

....

What is the first step to take to obtain this?

....

....

On a scale of 1 to 10, with 10 being the most and 1 being the least, how fulfilled would you say you are right now and why?

....

....

Focus on the journey, not the destination.

When you're on the go, what do you do to make the journey more enjoyable?

....

....

Name some songs on your travel playlist:

....

....

Which snacks do you eat?

....

....

Preferred mode of Transportation:

....

....

Ideal time to travel and why?

....

....

Exciting Upcoming Events

List the events below:

-
-
-
-
-
-
-
-
-
-

Which of these events are you most excited about? Why?

CHEER YOURSELF UP!

List five activities that always cheer you up.

....

....

Out of the five activities, which one cheers you up the most and why?

....

....

Is there a person in your life who always makes you feel better?

....

....

What advice would you give to yourself to overcome sadness?

....

....

Today is a Happy Day!

Name one thing you can see that makes
you happy.

....

Name one thing you can touch that makes
you happy.

....

Has a person made you happy today?
If so, how?

....

....

....

What else could you do today to make
yourself happy?

....

....

....

Attitude of Gratitude

List five things that you are grateful for:

....

....

....

Out of the five things, which are you most grateful for and why?

....

....

What are you most grateful for this week?

....

....

Why do you think that having gratitude is so important?

....

....

give yourself

permission to

be happy

every day

ON A SCALE OF 1 TO 10

(10 BEING THE MOST, 1 BEING THE LEAST),
RATE HOW HAPPY EACH OF THESE THINGS MAKE YOU:

DRAW A LINE FROM EACH THING TO THE NUMBER

1	2	3	4	5	6	7	8	9	10

MY HOMETOWN

MY DAILY ROUTINE

MY HOME LIFE

MY WEEKENDS

MY HOBBIES

MY RELATIONSHIPS WITH OTHERS

MY JOB

MY FASHION SENSE

WHAT THINGS IN LIFE MAKE YOU 10/10 HAPPY?

MY SHORT-TERM GOALS

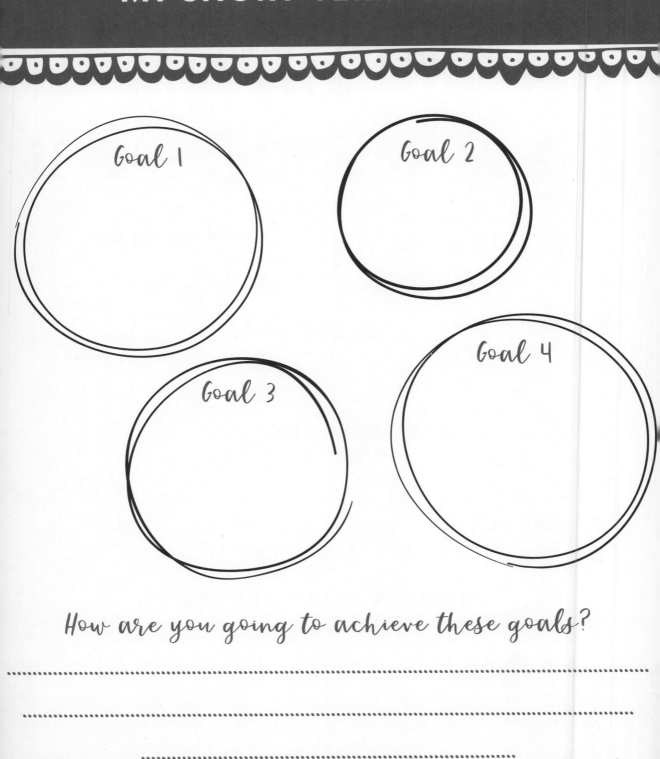

Goal 1

Goal 2

Goal 3

Goal 4

How are you going to achieve these goals?

....

....

....

Why is achieving these goals important to you?

....

....

....

Goal 1

Goal 2

Goal 3

Goal 4

MY LONG-TERM GOALS

CREATE FIVE HAPPINESS-FILLED SOCIAL MEDIA POSTS BELOW:

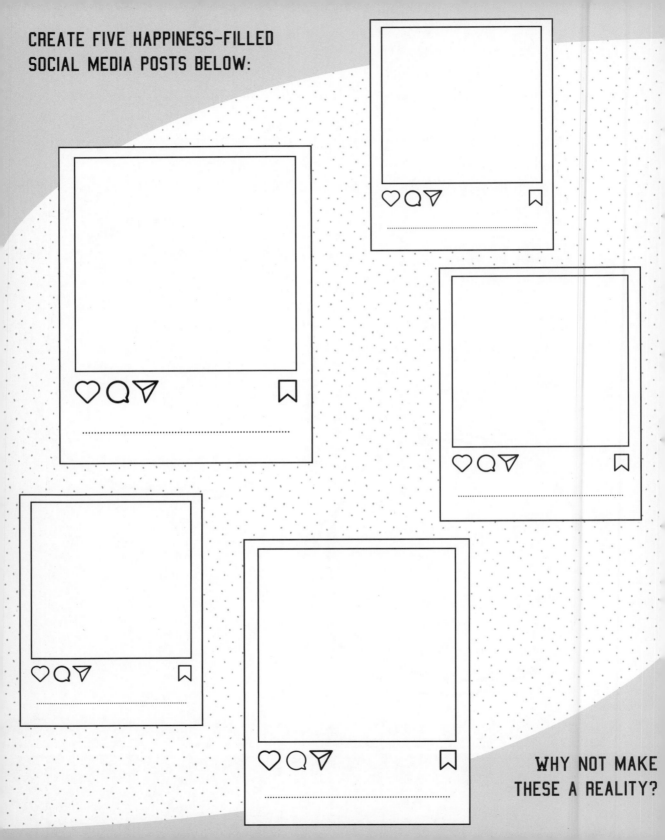

WHY NOT MAKE THESE A REALITY?

My Priorities
in Life

What is your number one priority right now?

....

....

What are three other priorities you have?

....

....

Why do you consider each of these things
a priority?

....

....

....

Is there anything you need to make more
of a priority?

....

....

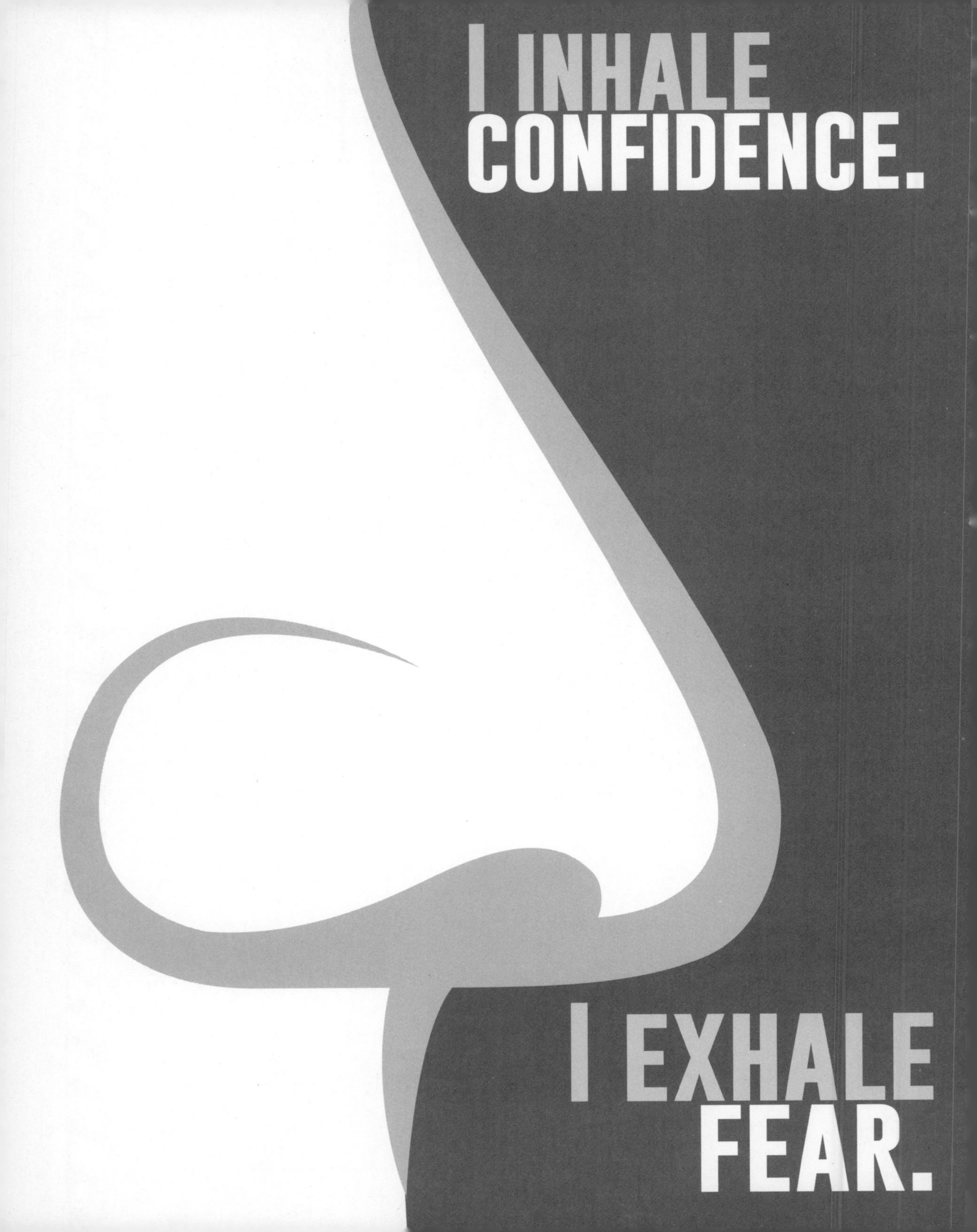
I INHALE
CONFIDENCE.
I EXHALE
FEAR.

CONFIDENCE
AND ME

ON A SCALE OF 1 TO 10, 10 BEING THE MOST AND 1 BEING THE LEAST, HOW CONFIDENT WOULD YOU SAY YOU ARE CURRENTLY AND WHY?

....

....

....

WHICH AREAS OF YOUR LIFE DO YOU FEEL THE MOST CONFIDENT IN?

....

....

....

WHICH AREAS OF YOUR LIFE DO YOU FEEL THE LEAST CONFIDENT IN?

....

....

....

....

WHAT DO YOU NEED TO DO TO START TO FEEL MORE CONFIDENT?

....

....

....

....

1 2 3 4 5 6 7 8 9 10

Imagine you're climbing a mountain to happiness.

What's at the top of it?

Draw a picture of it in this square:

WHAT OBSTACLES ARE CURRENTLY IN THE WAY OF YOU REACHING THE TOP OF THE MOUNTAIN? ADD THEM TO YOUR DRAWING.

MY TRUE PASSIONS IN LIFE

List five things you are passionate about:

....

....

Out of the five things, which are you most
passionate about and why?

....

....

....

Which of your passions would you like to
explore more of and why?

....

....

....

What is something that you think you
could develop a passion for?

....

....

....

WHO ARE THE HAPPIEST PEOPLE IN YOUR LIFE?

NAME.........................
WHAT MAKES THEM HAPPY?

....

DESCRIBE A HAPPY MEMORY YOU HAVE WITH THEM:

....

....

....

NAME.........................
WHAT MAKES THEM HAPPY?

....

DESCRIBE A HAPPY MEMORY YOU HAVE WITH THEM:

....

....

....

NAME.........................
WHAT MAKES THEM HAPPY?

....

DESCRIBE A HAPPY MEMORY YOU HAVE WITH THEM:

....

....

....

THE FAME GAME

IF YOU COULD MEET THREE FAMOUS PEOPLE, LIVING OR DEAD, WHO WOULD YOU CHOOSE?

....

....

....

WHY DID YOU CHOOSE THESE THREE?

....

....

....

WHAT IMPACT HAVE THEY HAD ON YOU?

....

....

....

WHICH QUESTIONS WOULD YOU ASK?

....

....

....

Be your own kind of Beautiful

You are wonderful.

List five positive traits your loved ones
would say you have:

....

....

Name something that you're insanely good at doing:

....

....

Which compliment would you give to yourself?

....

....

If you could give yourself 10/10 for something,
what would it be?

....

....

Create a bucket list of things you would like to do in your life.

Now that you have your list, answer the questions below:

Which three things will bring you the most joy when you check them off?

....

....

....

Which things will you do with other people and which will you do alone?

....

....

....

What do you plan to check off first?

....

....

....

Do you have a time frame for completing your bucket list? Explain your answer.

....

....

....

WHAT'S IN YOUR WARDROBE?

LIST SOME OF THE ITEMS IN YOUR WARDROBE:

WHICH OUTFIT DO YOU FEEL MOST CONFIDENT IN AND WHY?

....

....

DO YOU HAVE ANY SPECIAL ITEMS IN YOUR WARDROBE?

....

....

WHAT ARE THEY?

....

....

HOW WOULD YOU DESCRIBE YOUR SENSE OF FASHION?

....

....

WHICH ITEM OF CLOTHING WOULD YOU LOVE TO ADD TO YOUR WARDROBE?

....

....

WHAT'S IN YOUR BAG?

LIST ALL OF THE ITEMS IN YOUR BAG:

WHAT DO YOU THINK THE ITEMS SAY ABOUT YOU?

....

....

WHICH OF THE ITEMS IS THE MOST IMPORTANT TO YOU? WHY?

....

....

WHICH OF THE ITEMS IS THE MOST OBSCURE? DESCRIBE IT BELOW:

....

....

POSITIVE MIND
POSITIVE VIBES
POSITIVE LIFE

WRITE DOWN AS MANY SONG LYRICS YOU CAN THINK OF
THAT USE THE WORD "HAPPY". IF YOU'RE STRUGGLING,
WRITE DOWN ANY SONG LYRICS THAT MAKE YOU FEEL HAPPY.
DOODLE AROUND THEM AS MUCH AS YOU LIKE!

THINK ABOUT YOUR GUILTY PLEASURES.

What is your number one guilty pleasure?

....

List three more guilty pleasures you have:

....

Why do you enjoy these so much?

....

....

....

How do guilty pleasures make you feel?

....

....

....

....

....

REMEMBER THAT TIME YOU LAUGHED UNTIL YOU CRIED?

When was this and what happened?

....

....

Why did it make you laugh so much?

....

....

....

What were other people's reactions?

....

....

....

How often do you experience this feeling?

....

....

How do you usually interact with others?

....

....

....

What was the last phone call you had
that made you happy?

....

....

What was the last social media interaction
that made you happy?

....

....

Who would you like to reach out to that you
haven't talked to in a while?

....

....

....

Note down some fun ideas about how to make your closest friend or partner happy..

Idea 1:

....

Steps to be taken:

....

....

Idea 2:

....

Steps to be taken:

....

....

Idea 3:

....

Steps to be taken:

....

....

MY BODY IS SACRED
AND I WILL TAKE CARE OF IT.

My wonderful
wind-down routine

Write down some relaxing activities
that will help you prepare for sleep:

....

....

....

What will you wear? Dress for comfort!

....

....

How could you make your bed as comfortable as possible?

....

....

Create two evening mantras to help you relax.
For example, "My sleep will restore and rejuvenate me".

....

....

....

Use the shapes to write down what's inside and outside of your comfort zone.

Your Comfort Zone:

Outside Your Comfort Zone:

Do you ever feel like going outside of your comfort zone?

Which word or phrase
makes you feel happy?
Write it above in big
letters and doodle
all around it.

Imagine you are placing everything that makes you unhappy into a box.

List five things you would put in the box:

....

....

....

Create a positive mantra to repeat as you fill the box.
For example: "Everything in this box no longer serves me".

....

....

How do you hope to feel after the box is full?

....

....

How will you ensure that it can never be opened again?

....

....

Letting go and making changes

List five things you would like to let go of:

....

....

....

Which habits would you like to change?

....

....

Which emotions would you like to experience less of?

....

....

What is the first step you need to take toward removing anything that makes you unhappy?

....

....

REWARDING YOURSELF

What would you like to reward yourself for?

....

....

How could you reward yourself?

....

....

Why do you think it's important to acknowledge your achievements?

....

....

Think of a special reward for a future achievement:

....

....

IMAGINE THAT TODAY IS THE HAPPIEST DAY OF YOUR LIFE

What is happening?

....

....

....

Where is it taking place?

....

....

....

What makes it such a special day?

....

....

....

How does the day begin and end?

....

....

....

WHICH SEASON DO YOU ASSOCIATE WITH HAPPINESS?

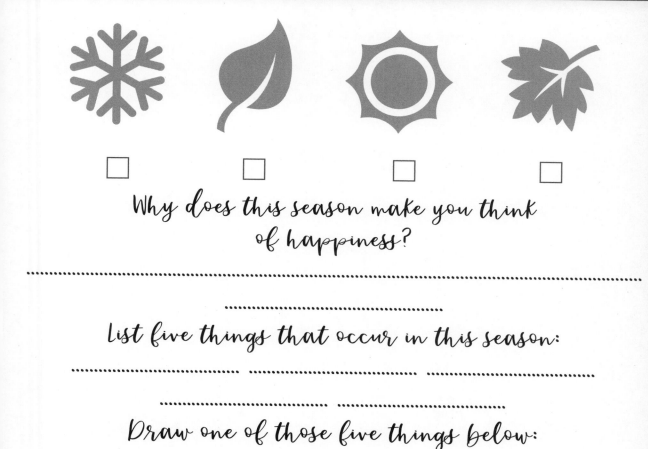

☐ ☐ ☐ ☐

Why does this season make you think of happiness?

....

....

List five things that occur in this season:

....

....

Draw one of those five things below:

Complete the following sentences about your happiness.

The thing that is making me happiest right now is:

....

....

....

....

....

....

I desire to feel happier about:

....

....

....

....

....

....

....

....

In order to feel happier more often, I can:

....

....

....

....

....

One way that I make myself feel happy is:

....

....

What is one thing you would love to be doing this time next year?

....

....

....

....

....

....

Complete the following sentences about your future.

Which areas of your life would you like to see improvements in? Why?

....

....

....

....

....

....

....

....

What would you like to continue doing?

....

....

....

....

Create a positive affirmation to make this happen:

....

....

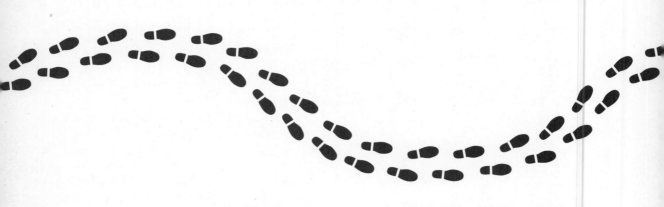

If you walk in joy,
happiness is close behind.

SKETCH YOUR PERFECT OUTDOOR VIEW. IS IT A GARDEN FILLED WITH FLOWERS OR THE SUN SETTING OVER A LAKE? BE AS CREATIVE AS YOU LIKE!

List two people who you think could use a happy thought:

Write down a happy thought to send to each of them.

Sending out happy thoughts

Think of a happy thought for someone you haven't connected with in a while:

Note down a happy thought you'd like to get from someone else:

Creating and maintaining a happy mindset

How would you describe your mindset right now?

Which exercises could you do to create a happier mindset?

What could you do to maintain a happy mindset?

What does having a happy mindset mean to you?

Create seven morning mantras to help
you start your day as positively as possible.
For example, "I am powerful".

Focus on one each morning and say it
out loud to set a positive intention for the day.

Project Happy

Think of a project that would bring you lots of happiness.
It could be a DIY task or a personal one, such as working
on your health and well-being.

Describe your happiness project:

....

....

....

....

Draw what you imagine the end result will look like:

How would this project improve your current state of happiness?

....

....

....

I have the
power to choose
to be happy

This is your happiness cake. Label each layer with a different type of cake that makes you happy. Can you think of when you last tasted it?

Happy Ratings

How happy do each of the following activities make you?

Draw a line from the activity to the chosen number.

Spending time with family

Spending time alone

Going on a trip

Spending time outdoors

Playing sports or working out

1 2 3 4 5

Attending parties

Getting coffee with someone

Using social media

Going to a live event

Doing household chores

If you have given any of the activities a 10, why?

....

....

....

Eating in a
restaurant

Reading a book

Watching TV

Meeting up with
friends

Watching a movie

6 7 8 9 10

Cooking

Going shopping

Taking weekend trips

Working on a project

Name some 10/10 activities to do in your spare time:

....

....

....

NEXT WEEK'S SCHEDULE
FILL IN THE CALENDAR WITH ALL OF YOUR
UPCOMING PLANS AND IMPORTANT DATES.

WEEK OF _____

MONDAY

TUESDAY

WEDNESDAY

THURSDAY

FRIDAY

SATURDAY

SUNDAY

GOALS

_____

_____

_____

_____

_____

TO DO LIST

_____

_____

_____

_____

NOTES

_____

_____

_____

_____

WHERE COULD YOU ADD THINGS TO MAKE NEXT WEEK A HAPPIER ONE?

MONDAY

TUESDAY

WEDNESDAY

THURSDAY

FRIDAY

SATURDAY

SUNDAY

WEEK OF _____

GOALS

_____
_____
_____
_____
_____
_____
_____

TO DO LIST

_____
_____
_____
_____
_____
_____

NOTES

_____
_____
_____
_____
_____
_____

A smile is the beauty of the soul

MIRROR, MIRROR ON THE WALL

LIST FIVE OF YOUR MOST ATTRACTIVE FEATURES:

....

....

HOW DO YOU FEEL WHEN YOU LOOK AT YOUR REFLECTION?

....

....

NAME TWO THINGS ABOUT YOUR REFLECTION THAT ARE TOTALLY UNIQUE TO YOU:

....

....

CREATE A POSITIVE AFFIRMATION TO SAY TO YOURSELF AS YOU LOOK IN THE MIRROR:

....

....

Ten reasons why...
I am worthy of receiving love:

1 ....

2 ....

3 ....

4 ....

5 ....

6 ....

7 ....

8 ....

9 ....

10 ....

Ten reasons why...
I deserve to be happy:

1 ....

2 ....

3 ....

4 ....

5 ....

6 ....

7 ....

8 ....

9 ....

10 ....

Imagine that happiness is a character...

What does it look like? Draw it below:

List five things about the character of Happiness:

....

....

Does the character appear in a book, movie,
TV show or game, and why?

....

Think of a catchphrase for Happiness:

....

....

How does their story go?

....

....

Super-Happy Superhero

Your super power is spreading happiness.
What kind of things would you do?

....
....
....
....
....

Where do you love to spread happiness the most?

....
....
....

Do you have any additional super powers?

....
....
....

Who are your arch-enemies?

....
....

HAPPINESS DEPENDS UPON OURSELVES

MY CORE VALUES

List five of your core values:

....

....

Do you feel like your life aligns with your core values? Why? Why not?

....

....

How can you ensure that your life is always in alignment with your values?

....

....

Which quality do you value the most in a person? Why?

....

....

Finding time for alone-time

Which activities do you love to do by yourself?

....

....

....

....

Where do you love to spend time alone?

....

....

....

....

Why do you think it's important to have quality alone-time?

....

....

....

....

Which new activity could you start doing by yourself?

....

....

....

THE GREAT OUTDOORS

Which sights and sounds do you notice around you when you are outside?

....

....

Which physical sensations do you experience?

....

....

....

Which emotions are you feeling?

....

....

....

Create a nature-themed affirmation to think about on your next walk:

....

....

....

This is the door to happiness.

What do you think is behind the door?

....

....

How do you feel as you stand in front of it?

....

....

What can you see through the keyhole?

....

....

Draw it here:

After opening the door,
what is the first thing you see?

....

....

....

What physical sensations do you experience?

....

....

....

Does anyone come to greet you? If so, who?

....

....

....

What is the first thing you do?

....

....

What is the first thing you say?

....

....

The less you care what others think, the happier you will be.

WHAT IT MEANS TO BE HAPPY

What do you think are the three key points to happiness?

....

....

....

How can someone be a happy person?

....

....

Is being happy something you can get better at?

....

....

Do you believe happiness is a choice?

....

....

NAME FOUR SUBJECTS YOU WOULD LIKE TO LEARN MORE ABOUT AND WHY:

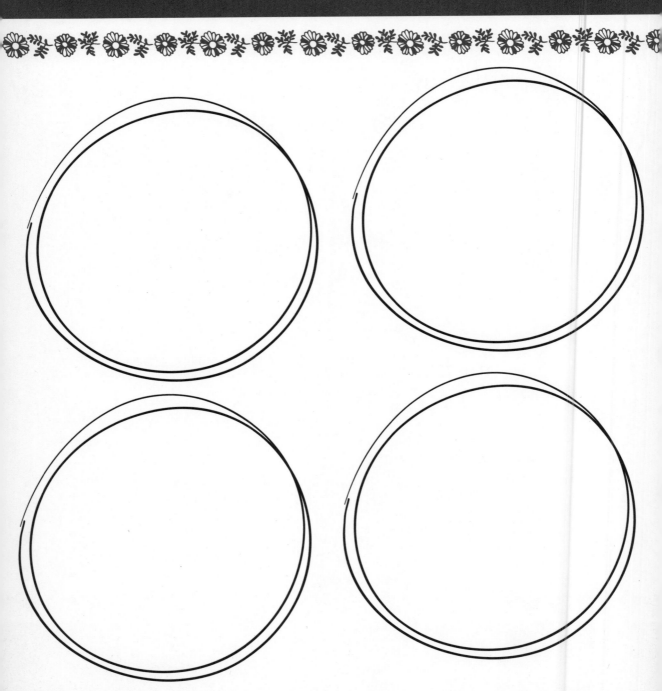

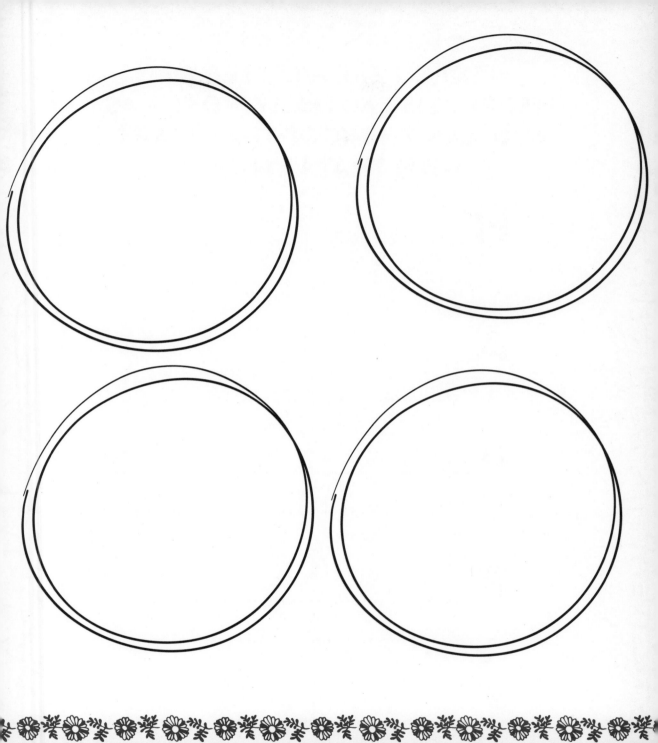

NAME FOUR WAYS TO
BOOST YOUR CREATIVITY:

NEXT TO EACH LETTER OF 'HAPPY', LIST AS MANY WORDS AS YOU CAN THINK OF THAT START WITH THAT LETTER.

H...

....

A...

....

P...

....

P...

....

Y...

....

Planet You

Imagine that you have your own planet.
What can visitors expect to find?

....

....

....

How do you take care of your planet?

....

....

....

What makes your planet unique?

....

....

....

Why is your planet such a happy
place to be?

....

....

"WHEN YOU FOCUS ON THE GOOD, THE GOOD GETS BETTER."

On-screen happiness

Choose five feel-good moments from movies or TV shows:

....

....

Why do these moments resonate with you?

....

....

Which of those five moments make you
the happiest?

....

....

Write down any other emotions that you experience
during these moments.

....

....

DE-STRESS AND DETOX

List some of the things that bring you stress:

....

....

....

Do you experience any physical symptoms during stressful times?

....

....

....

What activities help you to relieve stress?

....

....

....

What advice would you give to someone experiencing stress right now?

....

....

What is the one thing about yourself that you need to embrace more? Write it below and doodle around it.

SET A TIMER FOR 60 SECONDS.
DURING THIS TIME, WRITE DOWN AS MANY
HAPPY WORDS AS YOU CAN THINK OF:

CIRCLE THE FIVE WORDS YOU ARE DRAWN TO THE
MOST AND REFLECT ON WHY YOU CHOSE THEM.

SET THE TIMER FOR ANOTHER 60 SECONDS. WRITE DOWN AS MANY PEOPLE AS YOU CAN THINK OF THAT MAKE YOU HAPPY:

CIRCLE FIVE PEOPLE YOU WOULD LIKE TO SEE IN THE FUTURE. HOW CAN YOU MAKE THIS HAPPEN?

Do more of what makes you

happy

This is your key to happiness. Write down all the
things you can do and say to unlock the way to a happy life.

My dream journal

Are you someone who dreams vividly?

Can you remember any dreams you've had?

What would you love to dream about more?

Do you have any recurring dreams?

PREDICTIONS FOR MY FUTURE HAPPINESS

Visualize each thing as you write it down.

SO MANY QUESTIONS

Ask yourself five questions,
starting with the following words:

Who..?

When...?

What..?

Where..?

How...?

Write your answers below and
think about why you asked yourself
these questions.

....

....

....

....

....

Taking a Risk

What is the one thing you'd love to do but feel you never could?

....

What is stopping you from doing it?

....

....

How would it change your life if you did it?

....

....

How often do you take risks in life? Why?

....

....

Name something to do this week that's out of your comfort zone:

....

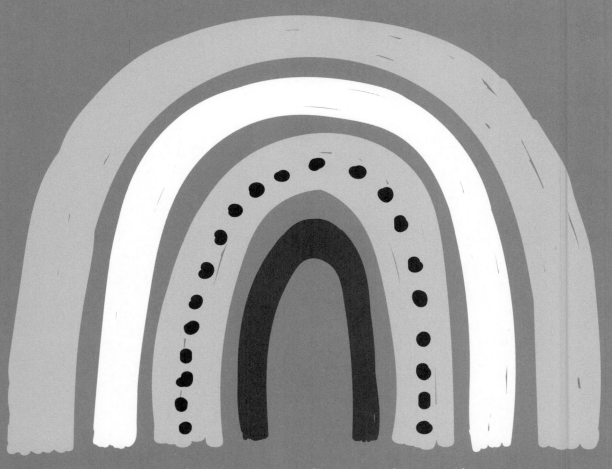

The greater the storm, the brighter the rainbow.

WHAT STRUGGLES HAVE YOU OVERCOME IN YOUR LIFE?

....

....

WHAT HAS HELPED YOU TO OVERCOME OBSTACLES IN THE PAST?

....

....

WHAT DIFFICULT LIFE LESSON HAVE YOU HAD TO LEARN?

....

....

HOW DID THIS LIFE LESSON HELP YOU GROW AS A PERSON?

....

....

WHAT ADVICE WOULD YOU GIVE TO SOMEONE WHO WANTS TO
FIND HAPPINESS IN DIFFICULT TIMES?

....

....

Gaining perspective

What is the main problem that you are experiencing right now?

....
....
....

Do you think this problem will affect you in six months?
Why? Why not?

....
....
....

Do you think this problem will affect you one year from now?
Why? Why not?

....
....
....

Imagine that you are looking at your life from a bird's-eye view.
Can you still see the problem?

....
....
....

What things make you smile? Think about it and write them all around this happy face!

Write down tons of positive thoughts around this smiling face. The more you can think of, the better!

BEAUTIFUL DAYS
begin with
BEAUTIFUL MINDSETS

Write a list of all the little things in life that bring you joy. It could be the smell of freshly cut grass, a smile from a stranger or a cold drink on a hot day!

. . . .

. . . .

. . . .

. . . .

. . . .

. . . .

. . . .

. . . .

. . . .

. . . .

. . . .

. . . .

. . . .

. . . .

Write a letter to someone who makes you happy...

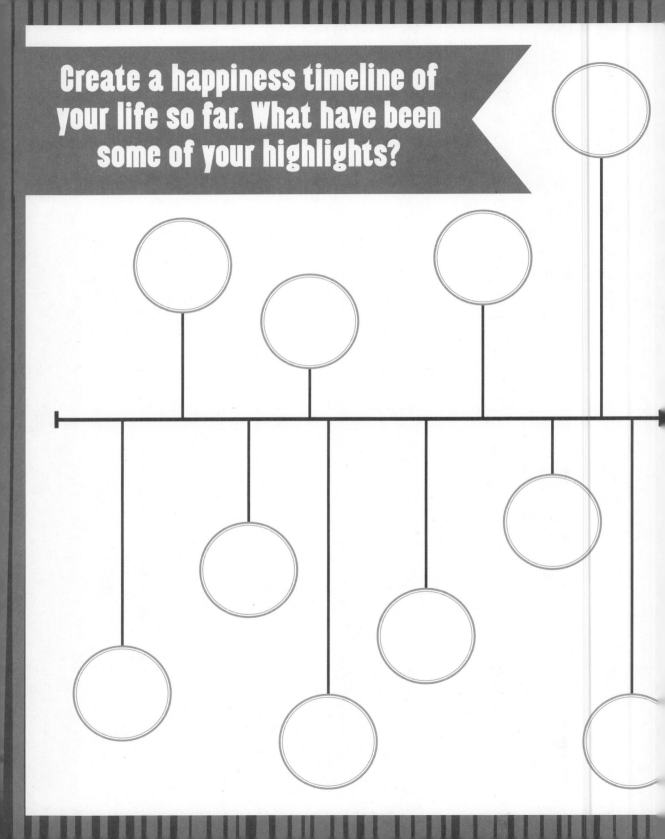

Create a happiness timeline of your life so far. What have been some of your highlights?

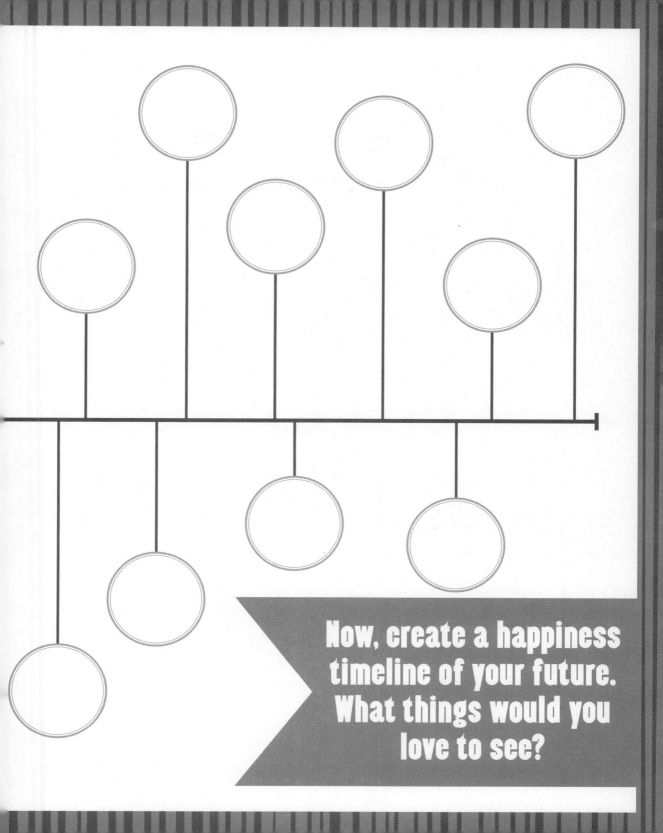

Now, create a happiness timeline of your future. What things would you love to see?

It's showtime!

Describe an amazing live performance you've seen:

....

....

....

How did it make you feel?

....

....

....

Do you prefer going to a play or a concert? Why?

....

....

....

Have you ever performed onstage?

....

....

....

THINK OF ALL OF THE THINGS THAT HAVE MADE YOU LAUGH THIS WEEK. LIST THEM.

WHICH PLANS ARE YOU LOOKING FORWARD TO? IF YOU DON'T HAVE ANY, MAKE SOME!

What keeps you motivated throughout the day? List five things below:

1

2

3

4

5

Out of the five, which one motivates you the most and why?

How would you motivate someone else?

I AM RADIATING SELF-LOVE AND ABUNDANCE

Love for
me, myself & I

What is something you truly love about yourself?

....

....

List five more things that you love about yourself:

....

....

Why do you think it is important to love who you are?

....

....

Create two self-love affirmations to say to yourself each day:

....

....

Peaceful Pause

Sit still and breathe slowly.
Answer the questions below and be in the moment.

Where are you?

....

....

....

How are you feeling?

....

....

....

What do you notice about your surroundings?

....

....

Write a list of everything you can see.
Place a check mark next to anything that brings
you joy and then reflect on why it does.

Make notes on everything you've learned
about yourself in this journal experience.
What makes you the happiest? What do you love most
about yourself? What does happiness mean to you?

ALL IS WELL IN YOUR WORLD

Find focus and contentment
with this five-minute meditation:

Sit or lie down in a comfortable position.
Close your eyes and take a breath in through your nose
and out through your mouth.

As you breathe, ask yourself:
What makes me happy?

Repeat the question a few times and gently
contemplate the answers.
Each time a thought comes into your mind that isn't
related to the question or your breath, quietly dismiss it.

Sit with these thoughts for a few minutes, then take
a long breath in and out, before opening your eyes.

Be happy whenever possible.

It is always possible.